Billy and the Anxiety Monster
How to Love Your Anxiety and Heal,
A Grown-Up Book for Your Inner Child

Billy and the Anxiety Monster
How to Love Your Anxiety and Heal
A Grown-Up Book for Your Inner Child

$20.00
ISBN 979-8-218-27362-0
52000>
9 798218 273620

ISBN: 979-8-218-27362-0
Second Printing 2023 -Convergence Healing
www.ConvergenceHealing.com

Disclaimer

The purpose of this book is certainly not to oversimplify anxiety, or any other condition. It is to share an idea, a process for healing and working through anxiety, that has been demonstrated as effective time and time again; that is approachable, repeatable, and doable. The process that Billy goes through is designed to encourage the individual to learn how to listen to the parts of themselves that are suffering and to tune into their own innate ability to heal. In no way is this process a substitute for medical or professional help.

Peter's work, the "Convergence Healing" process, the processes laid out in this story, are intended to help people discover their choices for healing, body, mind, spirit. Take what you like and leave the rest.

Much of the information here is based on the natural healing model rather than the medical allopathic model. While every caution has been taken to provide you with the most accurate information and honest analysis, please use your discretion before making any decisions based on the information in this book. Convergence Healing is not liable or responsible for any loss, inconvenience, or damage relating to your use of any of this information.

Acknowledgements

I am in deep gratitude for every Gryllus that I have met on my journey with my clients, including my own. Thank you for pushing me to heal in ways I never thought I could.

To my amazing family and beautiful friends, I am so grateful for your patience, kindness, and compassion.

Thank you, for loving yourself and reading this book!

ONCE UPON A TIME, THERE WAS A BOY NAMED BILLY WHO LOVED TO BE SILLY. BILLY LIKED TO LAUGH WITH HIS BELLY AND GIGGLE WITH HIS SMILE. WHILE HE HAD A HAPPY HEART.....

SOMETIMES BILLY FOUND HIMSELF FEELING NERVOUS IN GROUPS OF PEOPLE OR EVEN BY HIMSELF. HE WORRIED ABOUT SCHOOL MORE AND MORE, AND THE BELLY LAUGHS HAPPENED LESS AND LESS. HE WORRIED ABOUT HIS PARENTS, AND THE GIGGLES HARDLY HAPPENED ANYMORE. HE WORRIED ABOUT BEING GOOD ENOUGH IN SCHOOL, FOR HIS FAMILY, AND EVEN HIS FRIENDS. OFTEN, BILLY FELT A STRANGE FEELING, LIKE BEING LOST AND DISORIENTED, EVEN WHEN HIS FRIENDS OR FAMILY WERE RIGHT THERE.

One day, Billy's parents started arguing. Billy's mom was clenching her fists, and his dad kept stomping up and down. Billy thought to himself, "If I acted like this, I would be grounded!" Things got pretty bad, and all of these feelings flooded into Billy all at once. Billy stood there. What else do you do if you feel like you can't do anything?

In fact, Billy couldn't move. He tried to cry, but tears wouldn't come. He tried to yell and tell his parents to "Stop!" but his voice wouldn't work. He started to sweat and get red hot. At the same time, He felt an icy blue shiver run up and down his spine. His eyes were open, but he felt like he couldn't open them wide enough, and the world started spinning around him. When he forced his eyes shut, it was as if the yelling got louder inside Billy's head. He began to shake and wobble, and tears finally came as everything suddenly went dark.

BILLY OPENED HIS EYES A FEW MOMENTS LATER. HE WAS BEING HELD IN A BEAR HUG, SQUISHED BETWEEN HIS MOM ON ONE SIDE AND HIS DAD ON THE OTHER. BOTH WERE HOLDING HIM TIGHTLY, AND BILLY FELT BETTER! THE SCARY FEELINGS THAT OVERWHELMED HIM HAD FADED, AND THE RED-HOTNESS AND COLD SHIVERS WERE GONE. AT LEAST, FOR NOW.

A FEW DAYS LATER, BILLY WAS SITTING DOWN WITH HIS THERAPIST PETE, OR MR. PETE AS BILLY LIKED TO CALL HIM. BILLY SHARED HOW SCARED HE WAS A FEW DAYS AGO WHEN HIS PARENTS WERE ARGUING AND HOW HE DIDN'T UNDERSTAND WHAT HAD HAPPENED TO HIM. HE TOLD MR. PETE THAT HE WAS A LITTLE FREAKED OUT. MR. PETE ASKED BILLY A FEW QUESTIONS. HE EXPLAINED TO BILLY THAT HE HAD PROBABLY EXPERIENCED SOMETHING CALLED AN ANXIETY ATTACK. FOR BILLY, IT WAS MORE THAN JUST ANXIETY. BILLY FELT HE UNDERSTOOD THE WORD ATTACK DEEPLY, AND HE TOLD MR. PETE HOW AFRAID HE WAS THAT THIS ANXIETY ATTACK WOULD COME BACK. THEN MR. PETE ASKED BILLY A QUESTION THAT HE THOUGHT WAS REALLY WEIRD. "WHAT IF YOUR ANXIETY WASN'T A BAD THING?"

Billy thought about it for a moment, and he said, "If it was a good thing, I don't want to feel that ever again."

"Well," asked Mr. Pete, "What if the cold shivers and the heat that made you sweat were signals? What if they are your bodies way of removing you from something you don't like, something scary or unsafe?"

Billy thought about it for a moment and reluctantly said, "Well, it did get my parents to stop yelling at each other. And, it felt really nice to hear them tell me how much they loved me when they hugged me."

Mr. Pete asked, "So, although you didn't like the feeling of the anxiety, it actually did something good for you?"

"I guess," Billy admitted in a very doubting tone.

Mr. Pete asked, "What did the anxiety look like, Billy? I mean, if you were to draw it for me, what would it look like in your drawing?"

Billy took a moment to think this over. No one had asked him about this before, but he did remember a scary monster that he had seen in a book on Medieval history. It was a funny and strange little monster with big menacing eyes, wild fuzzy hair, and no arms! Most importantly, it looked highly capable of growling and snarling and making you feel really scared.

Billy said, "It would be a monster!"

"Okay," Mr. Pete continued, "Billy, you know how sometimes when you're hurt, you get angry and yell? Or, maybe you've punched someone before. Do you remember that time when you were so angry that you kicked your best friend?"

Billy sheepishly nodded.

"Well," Mr. Pete asked, "What if this anxiety monster was really upset, sad, or hurt? What if the anxiety monster simply felt ignored and, like you, didn't know what to do? What if it doesn't know how it is supposed to feel or what it is supposed to do, and it gets overwhelmed just like you can get overwhelmed at times?"

Billy took another moment. In spite of how uncomfortable he felt, he really tried to think about it deeply...

Then he said, "Hhhmmm... If I was like the anxiety monster, then I'd be sad. I'd probably feel frustrated and angry that no one was paying attention to me, and then I would probably get mad."

"So, would you say that the anxiety monster felt unloved?"
asked Mr. Pete.

"Yes!" said Billy, feeling hot.
"I bet the anxiety monster feels very unloved."

"I think you're possibly right," said Mr. Pete.
"What would it be like to give the anxiety monster a nice name?
Maybe we can call it 'Scary Billy' or..."

"No," interrupted Billy. "His name is Gryllus."

Mr. Pete smiled. "Why Gryllus?"

"Gryllus is the name of a medieval monster with legs and a head but no Torso," answered Billy. "The gryllus I saw was scary but also a little funny. He looks so funny even when he is scary, and he almost makes you laugh."

"Well then, Gryllus it is!" said Mr. Pete. "Would it be possible for Gryllus to be your friend? A friend who is just sad and maybe even angry, but still a friend?"

"Yeah," said Billy. " I can sure feel when he is upset."

"You know how your mom and dad hugged you when you were upset?"

Billy nodded, having an uncomfortable inkling of where this was heading.

"Well, it might be too much to hug Gryllus right now when he is scared, but I wonder what it would look like to be loving and even kind to him?"

"How?" asked Billy.

Mr. Pete told Billy a story about how he believes that all pain is actually a lack of love. He shared how when he feels loved, he can do anything. Knowing that he is loved gave Mr. Pete the courage he needed to do things he never had the courage to do before and to go places he never thought he would be brave enough to go to.

He reminded Billy of how afraid He was to jump off the high diving board last summer at the pool. How, when he finally saw his parents watching him standing up high on the edge of the board, even with all the other kids screaming and yelling at him, he felt better just knowing that his parents were watching and supporting him.

When his dad gave a big thumbs-up, and his mom nodded and smiled, he was able to jump into the pool! While it was no swan dive, Billy remembered how thrilling it felt and how he hadn't been able to make that leap until he saw his parents and knew they supported and loved him.

"Let's try this," suggested Mr. Pete. "How about you close your eyes and see Gryllus on the inside of your eyelids, like watching a movie screen in your mind? I'm right here supporting you, and you can open your eyes whenever you need to, okay? When you can imagine Gryllus being in the room right here with us, let me know."

Billy closed his eyes. After a few moments, he said,
"I totally see him! I see him!"

"And, how is he?"

"He's looking kinda angry, but I don't feel so afraid of his anger now. I even kinda want to giggle because he looks funny when he's angry. Uh-Oh, he doesn't like that. My laughing seems to make him angrier. He doesn't understand why I want to laugh."

"Great, Billy! So, what would it be like to say, 'I am sorry you're so angry, Gryllus? I'm sorry I laughed at you.'"

Billy paused, took a deep breath, and whispered, "I'm sorry you're so angry, Gryllus. I'm sorry. I don't like to be laughed at either."

A tear rolled down Billy's cheek, and Mr. Pete asked, "Is everything okay, Billy?"

"Yes. Gryllus is afraid of being laughed at."

"I get that. I'm sorry too, Gryllus."

"He's sad because I always try to ignore him when he's upset. He doesn't like it when I get mad at him when he's scared. He doesn't like it when I tell him to go away. He doesn't like it when he gets nervous, and I tell him to stop feeling that way. I don't like that either. Sometimes people tell me to stop being angry or to relax, and it always makes me angrier."

"I'm sorry for that, Billy," said Mr. Pete. "Sometimes, it's okay and even good to be angry. I wonder if your anger scares the people who are telling you to not be angry? Or, maybe they just don't feel comfortable being around anger? Just like you don't feel comfortable with Gryllus' anger."

"I didn't think about that," said Billy quietly. "I get really upset with my mom sometimes. She can be cranky. And when my dad gets angry, it scares me."

"I'm sorry for that too, Billy. I wonder what it would be like to give Gryllus permission to have his feelings? Would that be alright to do?"

"I suppose so," muttered Billy.

"When you say 'I'm sorry' to Gryllus, what does he do?"

"He changes. He doesn't look so angry, and his blue hair isn't so... frightful."

Mr. Pete giggled with Billy as Gryllus' physical appearance changed, along with his emotions. This was surprising to them both!

"Awesome, Billy! Now that Gryllus is changing and not so angry, maybe it would be okay to be more loving to him. What do you think?"

"I guess I could do that," said Billy. "But I still don't know about hugging him."

"Okay, you certainly don't have to. What if love was like taking a shower in golden sunlight? Do you think you can shower Gryllus in a loving, warm light like that?"

"That sounds strange, Mr. Pete," said Billy, "but why not?"

As Billy imagined Gryllus surround by beautiful rays of loving light, he started to relax. Billy didn't realize how his shoulders were up to his ears, and his brow had been furrowed. He didn't realize how he had been walking around with so much tightness in his body prior to talking with Gryllus.

"So, what's going on, Billy? I notice that your shoulders don't look so tense."

As Billy relaxed, so did Gryllus.

Billy opened his eyes and stared at Mr. Pete. "That was really weird, but I liked it. I actually feel better."

"Great," said Mr. Pete.

"I HAVE A HUNCH ABOUT MONSTERS LIKE GRYLLUS. MAY I SHARE THAT WITH YOU, BILLY?"

"SURE."

"WELL, I THINK THAT THE UNIVERSE IS CONSPIRING FOR US! DO YOU KNOW WHAT I MEAN WHEN I SAY THAT, BILLY?"

"NO. CONSPIRING? WHAT DOES THAT MEAN?"

"Some people think that the world is against them; that everything in life is happening to them; that life is a struggle, and that things like anxiety, like what you are experiencing, and even pain, are punishments or a bad thing. I look at anxiety and pain as something that is coming to teach us something."

"What do you mean?" asked Billy.

"Well, I used to have a lot of pain in my body, and I was really anxious and worried that I would always feel that way. When I started to look at the pain as a part of me that wanted to evolve, wanting me to be bigger and stronger, the pain started to ease up. It started to be less painful as I did that, and I felt less anxious too. I learned what it was trying to teach me."

"Oh!" said Billy. "So you think my anxiety is trying to teach me something?"

"I do," said Mr. Pete.

"WHAT DO YOU THINK IT IS?" ASKED BILLY.

"I DON'T KNOW. BUT I BET THAT GRYLLUS KNOWS WHAT IT IS!"

"REALLY? HOW DO I ASK HIM?" BILLY WAS THINKING OUT LOUD.

"Hhhmmm...there's a bunch of different ways, but I've found that the simplest way is to just close your eyes, invite Gryllus to sit down with us, and ask him."

"Really?"

"Yup. It sounds sort of simple, but it can really work if you're willing to listen. We're always talking at things like Gryllus. Maybe we can talk with him? What do you think?"

"I can try."

"Okay," said Mr. Pete. "Gryllus might speak to you through any or all of your senses. What I mean is Gryllus might actually talk to you through words, but he might also communicate with you through sounds, pictures that pop into your thoughts, and even smells and tastes. He has already been sharing with you through sensations like those cold shivers and hot sweats, remember that?"

THE MOMENT BILLY CLOSED HIS EYES, HE SAW GRYLLUS "POP" ONTO THE MOVIE SCREEN OF HIS EYELIDS IN HIS MIND.

"What is Gryllus doing right now?" asked Mr. Pete.

"He's sitting on the floor."

"And why is he sitting on the floor?"

"I don't know. He looks scared! Or annoyed. Or both. I don't feel so good right now."

"That's alright, Billy. I'm sorry you don't feel good. Is it okay to keep going?"

"Yeah, I guess so."

"Remember, if you ever want to open your eyes, that's okay. I'm here for you, and we can stop at any time. Does that work for you?"

"I guess," said Billy.

"All right then, let's keep going. You cool?"

"I got this," said Billy confidently.

"Awesome! So, why is Gryllus scared or annoyed and sitting on the floor?"

"I don't know," said Billy.

"Well, can you ask him?"

"I guess," sighed Billy. "Gryllus, why are you scared?"

Billy sat there for a moment feeling a little silly for talking to something that he only saw in his mind's eye. But, as he quietly focused on Gryllus, an understanding silently popped into his head.

He said,
"Gryllus doesn't always know what to do, and being on the floor in the corner feels better. Sometimes he feels overwhelmed like I do, and he just kind of freezes. Being on the floor helps him feel better."

"All right," said Mr. Pete. "Now that Gryllus is hanging out with us, I wonder if we can take our next step. What do you think, Billy?"

"Yeah," said Billy less than enthusiastically. Therapy was a lot harder than sitting around and talking about feelings. It's hard work!

"Gryllus is a part of you, Billy. He is the part of you that feels anxious and confused or even scared at times. And when that happens, he has those hot and cold feelings that you feel. When you feel that, you want to shut down those emotions, his emotions, right?"

"Yes," said Billy, suddenly adding guilt to his repertoire of differing emotions.

"Is it safe to say that Gryllus isn't so scary and that maybe he could be a friend of yours?"

"That could be cool."

"I'd like you to tell Gryllus that when he gets anxious from now on, you're not going to be mean to him and tell him to go away. Instead, if you want to, Billy, you're going to be nice to him and ask him what he needs, at that moment, right then, to feel better. Do you think you can handle that?"

Billy laughed and opened his eyes, saying, "Mr. Pete, you ask me to do the strangest things. You want me to be friends with my anxiety monster and to love it, and now you want me to ask it what it needs to feel better. Really?"

"Well, do you feel better?"

"Yeah...I guess I do," said Billy.

"Does Gryllus feel better?"

"This is a little freaky," said Billy. "Yeah, he does!"

"Are you willing to hang in there and keep going then?"

"Yes, I can do that."

"Okay. Close your eyes again and check in with Gryllus. How's he doing?"

"He's still sitting on the floor, but he's not in the corner anymore."

"Great! I want you to think about a time when you and Gryllus last felt anxious. Just nod your head when you have that thought."

Billy nodded, "I had a test at school last week that was really hard. I couldn't finish it because I freaked out, and I blanked."

"Perfect. I want you to focus on that past memory, Billy. Notice how Gryllus is doing."

"He's starting to get aggravated. He doesn't like failing. He feels embarrassed. He's starting to jump up and down."

"Now, press pause on that memory and turn to Gryllus. Like when you watch a movie and time stops. He's upset!"

"And I'm angry with him!"

"Good to know! With the memory paused for a moment, I want you to say to Gryllus, 'I'm sorry you're upset. I am too. We could have passed that test, and we didn't.' With time paused and you being nice to Gryllus, does this affect him?"

"HE'S...CRYING. I DON'T LIKE HIM CRYING. IT MAKES ME FEEL UNCOMFORTABLE AND ANGRY."

"WHEN YOU'RE UPSET AND CRYING, DO YOU LIKE IT WHEN SOMEONE TELLS YOU TO RELAX AND STOP CRYING...DO YOU?"

"NO!"

"Exactly. It's okay to be angry. The challenge is learning what to do with that anger. I wonder, though, instead of being angry with Gryllus, what would it be like to be kind to him? He's obviously hurting. Ask him what he needs right now, at this moment, to feel better."

"Okay...Gryllus, what can I do, right now, to help you feel better?"

Billy sat there, not saying much of anything. All this stuff was swirling around in his mind about his anxiety, his anxiety looking like a medieval monster, being loving to Gryllus, and now asking Gryllus, the anxiety monster, what he needed in order to feel better. It was nothing he would have thought of, but he thought to himself, "I do feel better!"

Billy took a deep breath and asked Gryllus again what he needed. Nothing came. Billy wasn't sure if he was doing this correctly, but he asked again, "Gryllus, what do you need from me to feel better?"

Gryllus just stared back at Billy. Maybe he doesn't know what to do either, Billy thought.

Then, something happened. Billy watched as Gryllus started to laugh, stand up, and dance! This made Billy laugh too.

Mr. Pete sat watching Billy be silly as he was giggling and wiggling around on the couch. He started to laugh. It was contagious, and soon everyone was laughing; Mr. Pete, Billy, and Gryllus. When things calmed down a little, Mr. Pete asked, "What was that all about?"

Billy said, "Gryllus wants to laugh and move around and be silly. He wants to play, and when he can't, he feels like he's stuck. Everyone is always telling him to back off and be quiet, and that upsets Gryllus. It could upset anyone."

"I see," said Mr. Pete. "Some people are very serious, too serious. Life has been hard for them, and they've forgotten how to laugh."

"That's sad. I'm good at laughing."

"I know! And sometimes it's not always appropriate to be silly and laugh and dance. I wonder if you could teach Gryllus when it is appropriate to laugh and dance and play and when it's appropriate to do that on the inside? In other words, Gryllus can always laugh and dance and play, but sometimes you might need to be still...at least on the outside. Like, when you take a test. What do you think about that, Billy?"

"I LIKE IT! AND GRYLLUS LIKES IT!"

"AWESOME! LET'S CHECK IN A LITTLE MORE WITH GRYLLUS. IS THAT OKAY?"

"YEAH...HE'S SO HAPPY!"

"FANTASTIC. AND HOW ARE YOU? DO YOU OR GRYLLUS FEEL AS ANXIOUS ANYMORE?"

"NOPE!"

"Cool! Would you be willing to dance around the room with me and Gryllus and celebrate him?"

"Mr. Pete, you are so bizarre, but why not? I like it!"

Mr. Pete, Billy, and of course, Gryllus began to dance around the room. They laughed, jumped on the furniture, and danced around. They were silly, and they played. Billy stood on the couch and stopped to take a breath while Mr. Pete collapsed in his chair, catching his breath.

"Would you be willing to try an experiment with Gryllus, Billy?"

"Okay."

"So, I want you to stand right there, take another deep breath, and calm your body as much as possible."

Billy stood balancing on the cushions of the couch. He closed his eyes and took a deep breath. As he did, his face relaxed and his shoulders dropped.

"Good. Now I want you to visualize, imagine, or simply think about being in class when it's time to take a test. This is one of those times that it is appropriate to be still...right?"

Billy nodded.

"Okay, now, while you're imagining taking the test, I want you to see Gryllus going through all your homework and finding the answers for you as he happily dances around. Let him laugh and be silly while you take the test. Maybe you can join him and tap your foot but stay as still as you can with the rest of your body. What do you notice?"

"I'm not sure what you mean."

"Well, in the past, when you were taking a test, you and Gryllus were very anxious and even upset at times. There were moments when you said you even felt angry and scared. What do you feel now? By the way, you can sit down if you'd like."

"Hahaha!" laughed Billy. "It was getting a little wobbly standing up on the couch." Billy sat down.

Mr. Pete asked again, "What do you notice as you take the test, and Gryllus dances around laughing and helping you to recall the answers to the test questions?"

"I feel more confident. I feel like I can know the answers when I've done my homework, and I've studied. Why shouldn't I be able to know the right answers?"

"Exactly. And, when you think about taking the test you have coming up next week, what do you notice?"

"I'm... not so anxious anymore! It's actually something that could be fun! All I have to do is sit there and let Gryllus deliver the answers."

"That's right!" said Mr. Pete. "I wonder if the anxiety you used to feel could be something that helps you achieve more in life? Like taking a test or even feeling your feelings without them being overwhelming and shutting you down. What do you think?"

"I think Gryllus could be a fun friend. I think we can learn a lot together!"

"I agree!" said Mr. Pete.

From that day forward, Billy knew what to do when Gryllus felt scared or upset. He knew that it was okay to have his feelings, and he even learned that his feelings, all of them, were important and were meant to be listened to and learned from. Billy had learned how to be present with his feelings even when he wasn't sure what he was feeling or even what to do next. He learned to tune into himself, into Gryllus, and ask what was needed in order to heal and feel better.

Over time, Gryllus and Billy became great friends. They learned to listen, understand, and work with each other. Billy and Gryllus went on many adventures together and never, ever stopped learning, loving, or listening to each other. Billy grew into a fine young man, a husband, and a father.

Billy learned how to manage his emotions and to be happy from deep within. Sometimes, Billy and Gryllus would pause and sit on the floor to reconnect and talk when things got tough. Other times, they needed to jump on the couch and be silly. Most importantly, as the years went by, whenever he and Gryllus felt anxious, they would always remember to pause and play, laugh and giggle, as they navigated through life together.

And Mr. Pete? Well, he had his own Gryllus, and they all lived and loved, cried, sang, and of course, danced through their anxiety happily ever after!

Steps for Knowing and Loving Your Anxiety Monster

1. Give your anxiety a shape or a form. It can be anything from a black cloud to the outline of a tree, a cube, roaring lion, lightning bolt, etc. (person, thing, historical figure, sense of nothingness). The only thing it can't be is someone who is still alive. If your anxiety shows up as a living human being (mom, dad, spouse, etc.), that's your Critical Mind getting in the way. You may feel they are the cause of your anxiety but step back and ask for another image to be presented to you. Anxiety is an internal experience. It is happening inside of you. Call for that internal experience to step out of you so that you can "see" it.

2. Give your anxiety a name. It may have your name, or it may not. Sit still, relax your mind, ask the question, "What is the name of my anxiety?" Let the first name that pops into your mind be its name.

3. Recognize your anxiety, introduce yourself to it and say "Hello". This is an opportunity to relate with this part that is suffering in a kinder, more honest, and direct manner.

(For the next few steps, be in a place of observation as much as possible. Notice how the following words affect your anxiety. Does it get bigger or smaller, louder or quieter, step forward or backward? Notice how speaking to it in the following words influences how it feels and shows up.)

4. Say "thank you" to your anxiety. We say thank you because this part of you is doing its best to protect you. It feels anxious and upset as a means to remove you from the stress you are having, or thinking about. It wants to protect you. You may not like how it's doing that, but it has a good intention beneath it.

5. Say to it, "I am sorry." We say I am sorry to the anxiety because we can often bully and beat it up. We shove the suffering down, ignore it, tell it to go away, and are often downright hostile to these parts of us. How would you feel if a part of you did that to you?

6. Next, say to your anxiety, "Forgive me for contributing to your pain in any way." Forgiveness is a way to put down the poisonous thoughts that continue the pain we are feeling. When we forgive, we create space in our minds and hearts and we can heal.

7. Say to your anxiety, "I love you". Continuing to shame, belittle, beat up, and withdraw love from this part of you only continues the pain. Your anxiety needs love more than anything! Shower it in love, give it a hug, let it feel the vibration of the words, send love to this part of you anyway you can.

(For the next three steps, don't worry if an answer doesn't come right away. Sometimes it will, sometimes it won't. Ask the questions and let them bounce around in your subconscious. An answer may come later as a dream, a moment of inspiration, a random thought, or even a color or image. Do your best to listen with all the tools you have (color, temperature, texture, sound, smell, taste, feeling). Use all your senses to "listen" for the answer.

8. Ask your anxiety, "What can I do to help you heal physically, in my body, right now?"

9. Ask your anxiety, "What can I do to help you heal mentally, in my mind, right now?"

10. Ask your anxiety, "What can I do to help you heal on the spirit level, in my heart, right now?"

(This is the beginning of a respectful, ongoing conversation. It is the starting point for you and the anxiety to work together and create a happier and healthier life for you both.)

11. Shake hands and come to an agreement, whatever that may look like, between you and the anxiety. Be in gratitude for how it is working with you and how you are relating differently with it. Say to it, "I am so grateful we are working together. I promise to be kinder to you and I know you are willing to be kinder to me. Thank you for calling me into a healthier relationship. I am grateful."

CONVERGENCE
HEALING
with Peter Bedard

Check out Peter's first book, "Convergence Healing, Healing Pain with Energetic Love", on Amazon, Kindle, or the audio book, through Audible.

For more inspiration you can also go to www.youtube.com/convergencehealing to watch hundreds of videos featuring Peter's work.

CONVERGENCE
HEALING
HEALING
PAIN WITH
ENERGETIC
LOVE

PETER BEDARD
WITH BRIAN SHEFFIELD HUNT

ENLIVEN

www.convergencehealing.com

Made in the USA
Middletown, DE
08 December 2023

45055674R00038